ExplOring maths

Home Book

1

Anita Straker, Tony Fisher, Rosalyn Hyde, Sue Jennings and Jonathan Longstaffe

Published and distributed by Pearson Education Limited, Edinburgh Gate, Harlow, Essex, CM20 2JE, England
www.longman.co.uk

First published 2009

ISBN-13 978-1-405-84405-5

Freelance development editor: Sue Glover

Typeset by Tech-Set, Gateshead

Printed and bound in Great Britain at Scotprint, Haddington

The publisher's policy is to use paper manufactured from sustainable forests.

Picture Credits

The publisher would like to thank the following for their kind permission to reproduce their photographs:

(Key: b-bottom; c-centre; l-left; r-right; t-top)

1 iStockphoto: Andrew Kendall. **2 Pearson Education Ltd:** Scott Foresman. **5 DK Images:** Dave King. **8 iStockphoto:** Amanda Rohde. **11 iStockphoto:** Jorge Delgado. **12 Pearson Education Ltd:** David Mager. **13 PunchStock:** Uppercut. **14 iStockphoto:** Christine Balderas. **16 Pearson Education Ltd. 19 Photolibrary.com:** Image Source. **20 Alamy Images:** Alan Copson City Pictures. **21 Alamy Images:** Tetra Images. **22 Alamy Images:** Colin Underhill. **23 iStockphoto:** (tr); Domenico Leoci (tl); Tom Hirtreiter (tc). **24 iStockphoto:** Andriy Zholudyev (tl) (tr); Joseph White (tc). **28 iStockphoto:** Alf Ertsland. **29 Alamy Images:** Keith Morris. **30 iStockphoto:** Denise Kappa. **31 Alamy Images:** Tony Cordoza (r). **Corbis:** Rick Gomez (l). **32 iStockphoto:** Alan Goulet. **33 Alamy Images:** Justin Leighton. **34 Jupiter Unlimited:** Photos.com. **36 Corbis:** Tom & Dee Ann McCarthy. **37 PunchStock:** Uppercut. **38 PunchStock:** Design Pics. **42 Art Directors and TRIP photo Library. 43 iStockphoto:** Vik Thomas. **45 DK Images:** Dave King. **46 iStockphoto:** Simon Podgorsek (r). **Pearson Education Ltd:** George Dodson (l). **47 DK Images:** (l). **PunchStock:** Brand X Pictures (r); Polka Dot (c). **49 DK Images:** Sarah Ashun (l). **Pearson Education Ltd:** (c) (r). **50 iStockphoto:** (r) (l). **58 Alamy Images:** TRG. **59 iStockphoto:** Dave White. **61 Pearson Education Ltd. 63 DK Images:** (c). **iStockphoto:** Dávid Pintér (l). **Jupiter Unlimited:** (r). **65 iStockphoto:** Lim Beng Chee (t); Steve McWilliam (b). **66 DK Images:** Tim Ridley. **67 iStockphoto:** Rafal Zdeb. **68 Alamy Images:** David J. Green - studio (l). **iStockphoto:** (c); Murat Koc (r). **70 iStockphoto:** (tr); James McQuillan (b). **Pearson Education Ltd:** Russ Lappa (tl). **72 Art Directors and TRIP photo Library. 73 DK Images:** Alan Keohane (c). **Getty Images:** Michael Simpson (r). **Pearson Education Ltd:** Anita Straker (tl). **74 Alamy Images:** Mike Hill. **75 Alamy Images:** graficart.net. **77 Pearson Education Ltd:** Bill Burlingham. **78 iStockphoto:** Sam Woolford. **79 Pearson Education Ltd:** Leslie Deeb. **81 Pearson Education Ltd:** Anita Straker. **82 Rex Features:** Nature Picture Library. **83 DK Images:** Stephen Hayward. **84 iStockphoto:** Gary Martin. **87 iStockphoto:** Andrew Johnson. **89 Alamy Images:** Phototake Inc.. **93 iStockphoto:** Chris Schmidt (b). **Pearson Education Ltd:** David Mager (t). **95 Alamy Images:** PHOVOIR / FCM Graphic. **100 Jupiter Unlimited. 104 DK Images:** Sarah Ashun (r). **Pearson Education Ltd:** (l)

Cover images: *Front:* **Alamy Images:** Kavita Favelle

All other images © Pearson Education

Picture Research by: Kevin Brown

Acknowlededgements

We are grateful to the International Olympic Committee for permission to reproduce data from "2004 Olympic Games in Athens Medal Table" published on www.olympic.org/uk/, reproduced with permission.

Every effort has been made to trace the copyright holders and we apologise in advance for any unintentional omissions. We would be pleased to insert the appropriate acknowledgement in any subsequent edition of this publication.

Contents

Properties of numbers

TASK 1: Multiples of 10

 **Points to remember**

⊙ Multiples of 10 end in 0.
⊙ To add or subtract a multiple of 10, count on or back in tens.
  The units digit stays the same.

1. Which are multiples of 10?

   307   210   600   703   370   125

2. Work these out.

   a 25 + 60   **b** 87 + 30   **c** 453 + 50
   d 90 − 50   **e** 76 − 40   **f** 128 − 50

3. Copy this.

   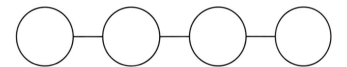

   Use all these.

   10   20   30   40

   Write one number in each circle.
   The difference between joined numbers must be more than 10.

 Did you know that...?

The Romans used the letter **X** for the number 10.

The tenth month in the Roman calendar was **December**.

A shape with 10 sides is a **decagon**.

A **decade** is 10 years.

TASK 2: Multiples of 2 or 5

⦿ Points to remember

⦿ **Multiples of 5** end in 5 or 0.

⦿ **Multiples of 2** end in 0, 2, 4, 6 or 8.

⦿ **Even numbers** are 0, 2, 4, 6, 8, 10, … They all end in 0, 2, 4, 6 or 8.

⦿ **Odd numbers** are 1, 3, 5, 7, 9, 11, … They all end in 1, 3, 5, 7 or 9.

1. Look at these numbers.

   252   340   25   876   90   134

   a   Which are multiples of 5?

   b   Which are multiples of 2?

2. Copy the grid.

   Cross out just two numbers.

   The rest of the numbers in each row and column
   must add up to a multiple of 5.

1	2	4	8
5	3	2	3
7	7	1	6
2	6	3	9

TASK 3: Odd and even numbers

 Points to remember

- odd − odd = even
- even − even = even
- odd − even = odd
- even − odd = odd

1 Which number is in the wrong place?

	multiple of 5	not a multiple of 5
even numbers	60	86
odd numbers	125	52

2 Which are odd multiples of 5?

390   213   685   370   705   493

3 Choose three of these digits each time.

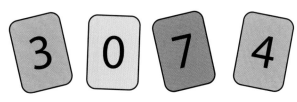

Make three-digit numbers.

a Make the biggest odd number.

b Make the biggest even number.

c Make the smallest odd number.

d Make the smallest even number.

Properties of shapes

TASK 1: 2D shapes

> ### ⦿ Points to remember
>
> ⊙ A closed shape with straight sides is called a polygon.
> ⊙ A shape with
>   - 3 sides is a triangle;
>   - 4 sides is a quadrilateral;
>   - 5 sides is a pentagon;
>   - 6 sides is a hexagon;
>   - 7 sides is a heptagon;
>   - 8 sides is an octagon.

You will need a piece of square dotty paper.

① This square has a pattern.

- ⬛ The yellow shapes are rectangles.
- ⬛ The green shape is a square.
- ⬛ The red shapes are large right-angled triangles.
- ⬛ The purple shapes are small right-angled triangles.
- ⬛ Each orange shape is a trapezium.

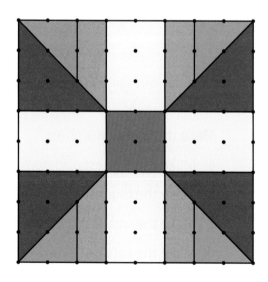

Draw a square with sides 8 cm long on dotty paper.

Draw a pattern in the square.
Use different shapes.

Use colour to show which shapes are the same.

Write down the names of all the shapes you used.

TASK 2: 3D shapes

Points to remember

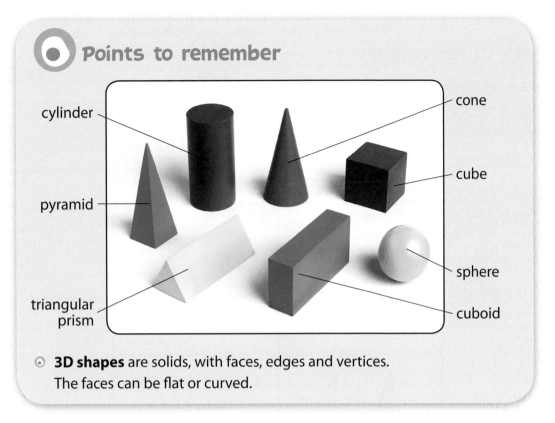

cylinder

cone

pyramid

cube

triangular prism

sphere

cuboid

⊙ **3D shapes** are solids, with faces, edges and vertices.
The faces can be flat or curved.

1. Copy and complete this table.

	number of **flat** surfaces	number of **curved** surfaces
sphere		
cone		
cuboid		
cylinder		

2. Copy these. Fill each gap with the right number.

 a A cube has ...... faces.

 b A cube has ...... edges.

 c A cube has ...... vertices.

3. Anna is thinking of a 3D shape.

 It has a square base.
 It has four other faces, which are triangles.

 What is the name of the 3D shape?

TASK 3: Angles and lines

⦿ Points to remember

⊙ A **right angle** is a quarter of a whole turn.

⊙ Horizontal and vertical lines are at right angles to each other.

1 One shape is in the wrong place on this diagram. Which shape is it?

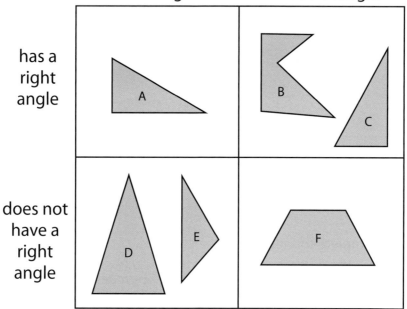

2 Here are some shapes on a square grid.

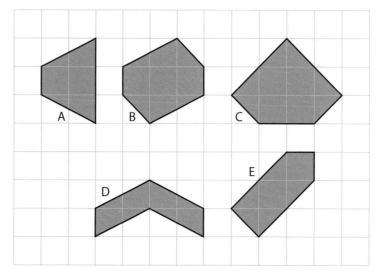

    a Write the letters of two shapes that are hexagons.

    b Write the letters of two shapes that have right angles.

TASK 4: Identifying positions

 Points to remember

To give the position of a square on a grid, write:

- ☉ the letter for the column and
- ☉ the number for the row.

You will need some squared paper.

1. The grey square is at position A2.

   Write the positions of the other five coloured squares.

2. Copy this grid on squared paper.

   Colour in these squares:

   B2, D4, C3, B4 and D2.

Adding and subtracting

TASK 1: Place value, ordering and rounding

> **Points to remember**
>
> ⊙ To order numbers, look at the digits.
> ⊙ < means 'less than' and > means 'more than'.
> ⊙ Round up fives, e.g. 425 rounds to 430.

1 Write in figures:

   a four hundred and thirty-six   **b** five hundred and nine

   c six hundred and eighty   **d** nine hundred and eighteen

2 214 written in hundreds, tens and ones is $214 = 200 + 10 + 4$

   Write in hundreds, tens and ones:

   a 315   **b** 450   **c** 803

3 Round to the nearest 10:

   a 536   **b** 273   **c** 485

4 Use these cards. Make three-digit numbers bigger than 500.

   Write each number you make in your book.

> **Did you know that...?**
>
> Chinese people used an abacus to help them to do sums.
>
> Most people now use calculators.
>
> An abacus is still used in some small shops and markets in China.

TASK 2: Number facts to 20

 Points to remember

⊙ Pairs with a sum of 10 are
   $0 + 10, 1 + 9, 2 + 8, 3 + 7, 4 + 6$ and $5 + 5$.

⊙ Use facts you know to work out others.

⊙ To add numbers like 8 and 6, bridge through 10.

⊙ When you add, start with the biggest number.

⊙ Learn number facts to 20 by heart.

1 Use two of these each time.

Copy and complete:

a ...... + ... = 14　　　　**b** ...... + ... = 16

c ...... + ... = 11　　　　**d** ...... + ... = 15

e ...... + ... = 13　　　　**f** ...... + ... = 17

2 Draw two big rings.

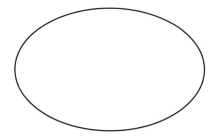　　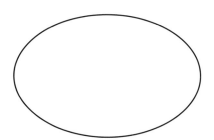

Use each number 2, 3, 4, 5, 6 once.

Write each number in one of the rings.

Each ring must have the same total.

TASK 3: Mental strategies

 Points to remember

- You can add numbers in any order.
- To add in your head:
  - start with the biggest number.
  - bridge through a multiple of 10.
- Draw a number line to explain your method.

1 Do these **in your head**.

Write the answer.

a 23 + 8   b 47 + 5   c 33 + 9

d 68 + 7   e 59 + 4   f 75 + 6

2 Use only these each time.

| 5 | 6 | 7 |

Work out where they go.

Write each sum.

a ☐☐ + ☐ = 63

b ☐☐ + ☐ = 81

c ☐☐ + ☐ = 72

TASK 4: More mental strategies

 **Points to remember**

⊙ To take away, bridge through a multiple of 10.

⊙ Draw a number line to explain your method.

1 Do these **in your head**. Write the answer.

    a 28 − 9   **b** 41 − 5

    c 23 − 8   **d** 94 − 7

    e 52 − 4   **f** 73 − 6

2 Ali went to the market.

Item	Price
onions	69p
carrots	34p
red cabbage	50p
broccoli	72p
beans	67p
lettuce	28p

Find Ali's change from £1 for:

    a onions   **b** carrots

    c a red cabbage   **d** broccoli

    e beans   **f** lettuce

TASK 5: Addition

 Points to remember when you add

- Look first at the numbers.
- Do it in your head if you can.
- Estimate the answer so you can check it.
- To add in columns, line up the digits.
  Put units under units, tens under tens, ...

Do these **without a calculator**. Show your working.

1. Work these out.

   a 135 + 68

   b 469 + 351

   c 96 + 37 + 59

2. Salma buys juice and crisps.

   The juice costs 87p.
   The crisps cost 38p.

   What is the total cost?

3. There is 157 ml of juice in a glass.

   Salma pours in another 85 ml of juice.

   How much juice is in the glass now?

4. The crisps weigh 25 grams.
   The glass weighs 87 grams.
   The juice weighs 465 grams.

   What do they weigh altogether?

TASK 6: Subtraction

 Points to remember when you subtract

⊙ Look first at the numbers.

⊙ Do it in your head if you can.

⊙ Estimate the answer so you can check it.

⊙ To subtract in columns, line up the digits.
Put units under units, tens under tens, ...

⊙ Count up from the smaller number.

Do these **without a calculator**. Show your working.

1. Work these out.

    a 127 − 54

    b 458 − 210

    c 731 − 258

2. John is 143 cm tall.
His dad is 190 cm tall.

    How much taller than John is his dad?

3. John's trousers cost £18.
His dad's trousers cost £42.

    How much less did John's trousers cost?

4. A flight to Spain is £136 for an adult.
It is £86 for a child.

    What is the difference between the cost
for John and the cost for his dad?

5. John's dad collects stamps.
He has 918 stamps altogether.

    He gave John 125 of his stamps.

    How many stamps did he have left?

TASK 7: Word problems

1. Katie buys:

> 87 g of peanuts for 68p
>
> 75 g of popcorn for 53p
>
> 325 g of cheese for 92p

  a How much heavier is the cheese than the peanuts?

  b What is the total weight of the cheese and the peanuts?

  c What does Katie pay altogether?

  d How much change does Katie get from a £5 note?

2. Write a word problem for each of these.

  a 45 + 32

  b 100 − 54

  c 125 + 80

TASK 8: Calculator skills

 Points to remember when you use a calculator

⊙ Estimate the answer so you can check it.

⊙ When you enter a calculation, press ⌷=⌷ after the last number.

⊙ If you make a mistake, clear the display and start again.

Use your calculator.

(1) What is the total of the red numbers?

a

215	312	383
458	229	216
96	197	315

b

215	312	383
458	229	216
96	197	315

c

215	312	383
458	229	216
96	197	315

(2) Which three numbers should you choose to make a total of 999?

215	312	383
458	229	216
96	197	315

TASK 9: Number investigations

Points to remember

- Read problems carefully.
- Work systematically.
- Look for patterns.
- See if there is more than one answer.

① Carl weighs a box.

He uses one or more of these weights.

What does the box weigh?

Find all the possibilities.

② Pick three cards with a total of 15. You can use a card more than once.

You can do it in five different ways.

Find them all.

Patterns and sequences

TASK 1: Multiplication patterns

> ### ⦿ Points to remember
>
> ⊙ 3 groups of 5 is $5 + 5 + 5 = 15$, or $5 \times 3 = 15$
>
> ⊙ $3 \times 5 = 5 \times 3$
>
> ⊙ Answers in the 5 times table are multiples of 5.
>
> ⊙ The 4th multiple of 5 is $5 \times 4 = 4 \times 5 = 20$.
>
> ⊙ Learn by heart tables for 2, 5 and 10.

① A corner shop sells sweets.

snack bar	chews	toffees	lollipop
5p each	**2p each**	**3p each**	**4p each**

Write the answers.

a What is the cost of 7 chews?

b How much do 6 snack bars cost?

c How much altogether are 5 chews and 2 lollipops?

d Which costs more, 5 lollipops or 7 toffees?

e What is the total cost of 2 toffees, 3 snack bars and 1 chew?

f How much change do you get from 20p for 4 toffees?

g How many chews can you buy for 16p?

h Which two coins would buy you 10 lollipops?

i How many snack bars can you buy for 35p?

j Jane bought 10 snack bars and 10 chews.
  What was her change from £1?

TASK 2: Simple sequences

 **Points to remember**

⊙ **Multiples of 3** divide exactly by 3.

⊙ The rule for the sequence of multiples of 3 is 'add 3'.

⊙ This sequence goes up in steps of 4. The rule is 'add 4'.

    1   5   9   13   17 ...

① Copy these. Fill in the missing numbers.

   a 3, 9, 15, ◯, 27, 33, ◯, ◯

   b 82, 78, 74, ◯, ◯, 62, 58, ◯

   c ◯, ◯, 17, 20, 23, 26

   d 78, 76, 74, 72, ◯, ◯, ◯

   e ◯, ◯, ◯, 36, 32, 28, 24

TASK 3: More multiplication patterns

Points to remember

⊙ **Multiples of 4** divide exactly by 4.

⊙ Numbers in the 4 times table are multiples of 4.

⊙ 12 is a multiple of 3 and a multiple of 4.
It is in the 3 times table and the 4 times table.

⊙ Learn by heart tables for 3 and 4.

① Here are some multiples of 4 from 4 to 40. Which two are missing?

     12   4   24   16   40   36   28   8

② Write the answers.

   a 9 × 3   **b** 4 × 6   **c** 3 × 8   **d** 5 × 9   **e** 8 × 4

   f 6 × 5   **g** 4 × 7   **h** 2 × 10   **i** 5 × 8   **j** 9 × 5

   k 6 × 4   **l** 7 × 3   **m** 9 × 2   **n** 4 × 4   **o** 3 × 0

TASK 4: More sequences

1   The tables in a classroom are triangular.
    Three children sit around each table.

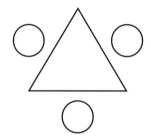

a   Copy and complete this table.

Number of tables	Number of pupils
1	3
2	
	9
4	

b   What do you notice about the number of pupils?

c   What is the rule?

d   How many pupils can sit round 6 tables?
    Explain how you know.

e   How many pupils could sit around 10 tables?
    Explain how you know.

TASK 5: Using number patterns to solve problems

⦿ Points to remember

- When you solve a problem, it may help to make a table.
- Work systematically.
- Work out the **step size** in a sequence.
  Use it to find the rule.

1. 28 is a multiple of several different numbers.
   Which numbers are they? Write them all.

2. There are 10 houses in Lime Street.

The milkman delivers 3 bottles of milk to some houses.

He delivers 5 bottles of milk to the rest of the houses.

Altogether, he delivers 42 bottles of milk.

How many houses get 5 bottles of milk?

How many houses get 2 bottles of milk?

TASK 6: Multiplying by 10 or 100

Points to remember

⊙ When you **multiply**:
   ×10, the digits move left 1 place;
   ×100, the digits move left 2 places.

⊙ ×100 is the same as ×10 then ×10.

⊙ To do 50 × 3, work out 5 × 3 then multiply by 10.

⊙ To change cm to mm, multiply by 10.

⊙ To change m to cm, multiply by 100.

1 Copy and complete.

a 5 × 10 = …   b 91 × 10 = …

c 6 × 100 = …   d 80 × 10 = …

2 Copy and complete.

a 10 × … = 610   b 10 × … = 700

c 8 × … = 800   d 100 × … = 500

e 52 × … = 520   f 10 × … = 900

TASK 7: Multiplying bigger numbers

 Points to remember

⊙ Use a grid for TU × U, and a calculator for bigger numbers.

⊙ Read problems carefully. Write down the sum you will do.

⊙ Do the sum. Use a calculator if you can.

⊙ If you do a pencil-and-paper sum, show your working.

⊙ Check your answer is about the right size.

⊙ Record your answer. Include units.

(1) Look at this grid.

The number at the top of the column is multiplied by the number at the left of the row.

For example, 6 is 2 × 3.

Copy and complete this grid.

×	2	5
3	6	15
2	4	10

×	7	8	9
4			
5			
3			

(2) Work these out **without a calculator**.
Show your working.

a   43 × 5

b   68 × 3

(3) You may **use a calculator**.

Bill is buying a new house.

The bank has lent him the money.

Bill will pay back £249 each month.

How much will Bill pay to the bank each year?

Angles and symmetry

TASK 1: Symmetry

⦿ Points to remember

- ⊙ If you can fold one half of a shape exactly on top of the other half, the fold line is a **line of symmetry**.
- ⊙ Shapes that can be folded in half in more than one way have more than one line of symmetry.
- ⊙ Some shapes have no lines of symmetry.

You need **G1.2 Resource sheet 1.1**.

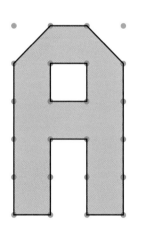

1. This letter A is drawn on dotty paper.

   Look at the capital letters on Resource Sheet 1.1.

   Draw the lines of symmetry on the letters.

2. Draw four different capital letters on Resource sheet 1.1.

   Draw any lines of symmetry on the letters.

ⓘ Did you know that...?

You often see lines of symmetry in the environment.

TASK 2: More symmetry

Points to remember

⊙ When you reflect a shape in a mirror line, the reflection is the same size and shape as the original object.

⊙ The shape and its reflection make a symmetrical pattern, with the mirror line as a line of symmetry.

1 Write the number of lines of symmetry for each of these.

a

b

c

d

e

f

g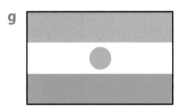

h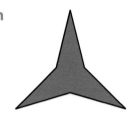

i

Did you know that...?

These tiling patterns have more than one line of symmetry.

TASK 3: Angles

① Make a right angle.

Fold a piece of paper once to make a straight line.

Press down to make a sharp crease.

The red dotted line shows the fold.

Now fold the red dotted line over on itself.

The blue dotted line is another fold.

Press down again to make sharp creases.

The corner where the red line meets the blue line is a right angle.

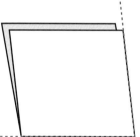

② Use your right angle to check these angles.

Which are more, which are less and which are equal to a right angle?

a

b

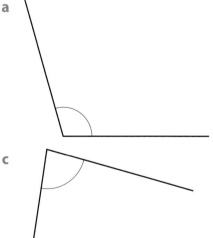

c

d

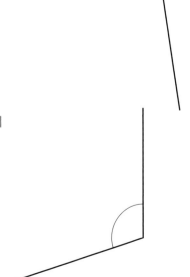

TASK 4: Moving on a grid

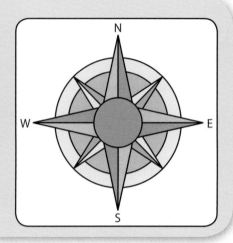

Points to remember

- The four main compass points are **north**, **south**, **east** and **west**.
- Compass points are used to give directions.

This map shows the occupants of nine houses.

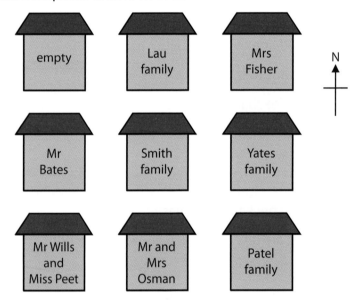

(1) Who lives east of the Smith family?

(2) Who lives north of Mr and Mrs Osman?

(3) Who lives west of Mrs Fisher?

(4) What direction is it from the Yates family to the Patel family?

(5) What direction is it from the empty house to Mrs Fisher?

(6) Who lives north of Mr and Mrs Osman but west of Mrs Fisher?

(7) Start at Mr Wills and Miss Peet's house.
Write directions to visit three other houses.

Multiplying and dividing

TASK 1: Doubling and halving

> **Points to remember**
>
> ⊙ **Doubling** is the same as multiplying by 2.
> ⊙ **Halving** is the same as dividing by 2.
> ⊙ To multiply by 4, double and double again.
> ⊙ To multiply by 8, double, double again and double again.

Do these **without a calculator**. Show your working.

1 Find half of these numbers.

    a 90   **b** 52   **c** 76

2 **a** Connor makes a sequence of numbers.

     His rule is 'double and subtract 5'.

     What are the next two numbers in his sequence?

            6   7   9   13   ...   ...

    b Jade makes a sequence of numbers.

     Her rule is 'subtract 1 from the last number then halve it'.

     What are the next two numbers in her sequence?

            63   31   15   ...   ...

3 Use doubling to work these out. Show your working.

    a 25×4 **b** 14×4

    c 12×8 **d** 9×8

TASK 2: Sixes and eights

 Points to remember

⊙ Answers in the 6 times table are double the 3 times table.
   Example: seven 3s are 21, so seven 6s are double 21 or 42.
⊙ Answers in the 8 times table are double the 4 times table.
   Example: fives 4s are 20, so five 8s are double 20 or 40.

Do these **without a calculator**. Show your working.

1. These numbers are the multiples of 6 from 6 to 60.

   Two multiples of 6 are missing. Which two are they?

   42   18   30   6   60   48   12   24

2. Big marbles cost 8p each.
   Small marbles cost 6p each.

   a What is the cost of
      4 big marbles?

   b What is the cost of
      3 small marbles?

   c What is the cost of 2 big
      marbles and 5 small marbles?

   d What is the cost of 5 big
      marbles and 10 small marbles?

   e Liam buys 6 small marbles.
      How much change does he get from 50p?

   f Olivia buys 6 big marbles.
      How much change does she get from £1?

TASK 3: Multiplication

Points to remember

- Use a grid to do TU × U and a calculator for bigger numbers.
- Read problems carefully.
- Write down the sum you will do.
- Do the sum. Use a calculator if allowed.
- If you do a pencil-and-paper sum, show your working.
- Check your answer is about the right size.
- Record your answer, with the units.

1 Work these out **without a calculator**. Show all your working.

   a   78 × 5

   b   69 × 4

   c   56 × 2

   d   83 × 3

2 You may **use a calculator**.

   a   Alice is paying for a new bike.
       She is paying £13 each week for
       24 weeks.

       How much will Alice pay for her bike?

   b   Alice rides 18 laps of the cycle track.
       Each lap is 475 metres.

       How far does Alice ride?

   c   Alice drinks 6 bottles of water during
       a ride.
       Each bottle holds 375 millilitres.

       How much water does Alice drink
       altogether during her ride?

TASK 4: Division and remainders

 Points to remember

- **Division** is sharing, or forming equal groups.
- $17 \div 5$ is 3 remainder 2.
  - The **divisor** is 5, the number you divide by.
  - The **quotient** is 3, the result.
  - The **remainder** is 2.

Do these **without a calculator**. Show your working.

(1) Write the answers.

     a $50 \div 5$ **b** $12 \div 4$

     c $21 \div 3$ **d** $45 \div 5$

(2) Write the remainders.

     a $48 \div 10$ **b** $25 \div 3$

     c $37 \div 5$ **d** $39 \div 4$

(3) Solve these problems.

     a Saeed has 24 geranium plants.
        He plants them in 3 rows.

        How many plants are in each row?

     b Rory has 26 seeds.
        He plants 3 seeds in each of his pots.

        How many seeds are left over?

     c Anna puts 4 seeds in each of her pots.
        She uses 6 pots and has 1 seed left over.

        How many seeds did she start with?

TASK 5: Dividing bigger numbers

Points to remember

- When you divide, estimate the answer first.
- Split up the number you are dividing to make it easy to divide.
- Record carefully what you do.
- Check the answer makes sense. Decide whether to round it up or down.
- Include units in your answer.

Do these **without a calculator**. Show your working.

1. Work these out.

   a 46 ÷ 3

   b 98 ÷ 5

   c 87 ÷ 4

2. a A carton of orange fills 6 glasses. Matthew wants to fill 50 glasses with orange.

      How many cartons of orange does he need to buy?

   b A bowl holds 4 oranges. Matthew has 23 oranges.

      How many bowls can he fill?

3.

   a Jo swims 5 widths of the pool. Altogether she swims 95 metres.

      How many metres wide is the pool?

   b A length of the pool is 25 metres. Jo wants to swim at least 180 metres.

      How many lengths should she swim?

Graphs and charts 1

TASK 1: Lists and tables

> ### Points to remember
> ⊙ You can use **lists** and **tables** to collect and organise information.

1 10 people named their favourite fruit.

This list shows the fruits they chose.

banana, grapes, pear, apple, pear,

apple, banana, grapes, apple, apple

  a Which fruit was most popular?

  b Name a fruit that no one chose.

2 The table shows pupils' house points:

Name	House points
Leah	7
Daisy	9
Joe	12
Rob	8
Cara	10
Jamie	8

  a Who has the most house points?

  b Who has more house points than Daisy?

  c Who has three more house points than Leah?

  d Which two people have the same number of house points?

TASK 2: Tally charts

 Points to remember

⊙ A **tally chart** helps you to sort and count data.
⊙ Each **tally mark** stands for one item.
⊙ Draw the tallies in groups of five, e.g.
  卌 stands for 5
  卌 III stands for 8
⊙ The total for the tally is the **frequency**.

1 Write the numbers for these tallies.

a 卌   b 卌 IIII   c 卌 卌 I

2 Draw tallies for these numbers.

a 8   b 15   c 13

3 Each pupil in a class chose their favourite food.

The tally chart shows the results.

Food	Tally	Frequency
Chilli	III	
Curry	卌 卌 I	
Chips	卌 I	
Pizza	卌 II	
Pasta	卌	

a What is the frequency for each food?
b How many pupils are in the class?
c Which is the favourite food in the class?

TASK 3: Bar charts

Points to remember

In a **bar chart**:
- both axes have labels;
- all bars are the same width;
- the length of the bar is the frequency;
- there is a gap between the bars;
- the bars can be horizontal or vertical.

You will need some squared paper.

1 A class of pupils chose their favourite food.

This table shows the results:

Food	Frequency
Chilli	3
Curry	11
Chips	6
Pizza	7
Pasta	5

a Draw a bar chart to show this data.

Make the bars 1 cm wide with a gap of 1 cm.

Number the vertical axis in 1s from 0 to 12.

b Which food was least popular?

c Which food did 7 pupils choose?

d How many more pupils chose curry than pizza?

TASK 4: Pictograms

 Points to remember

- You can use a **pictogram** to represent data.
- The pictogram must have a key to show how many items each symbol represents.
- The symbols should be the same size.
- The symbols should line up neatly.

Example

This pictogram shows the number of goals scored by some children in a football season.

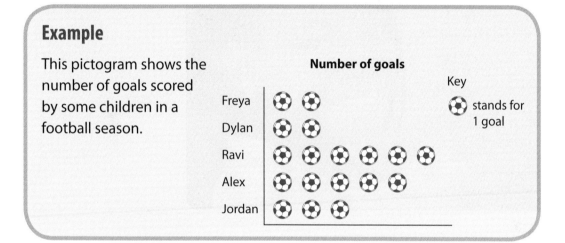

You will need some squared paper.

1. This table shows the number of goals scored by players in a hockey match.

Name	Number of goals
Liz	7
Billy	4
Stuart	3
Sanchez	0
Ella	4

a Draw a pictogram to show this data.
   Choose a symbol to stand for one person.

b Which person would you pick for your team. Why?

c How many more goals did Billy score than Sanchez?

Mental calculations

TASK 1: Quick ways to add and subtract

⦿ Points to remember

- ⊙ To add 9, add 10 then subtract 1.
- ⊙ To add 99, add 100 then subtract 1.
- ⊙ To add 90, add 100 then subtract 10.
- ⊙ To add 39, add 40, then subtract 1.
- ⊙ Make jottings if you need to.

Do these **without a calculator**.

1 Write the answers. Use jottings if you need to.

a 62 + 9	b 48 + 9	c 85 − 9
d 36 − 9	e 143 + 99	f 226 + 99
g 537 − 99	h 432 − 99	i 513 + 90
j 631 − 90	k 452 + 39	l 452 − 39

TASK 2: Adding and subtracting two-digit numbers

Points to remember

⊙ An empty number line helps you to do sums in your head.

⊙ To add, start with the larger number.

⊙ To subtract, count up from the smaller to the larger number.

⊙ Jump through multiples of 10.

⊙ If two numbers add up to 100, the units add up to 10 and the tens add up to 9.

Do these **without a calculator**. Write the answers. Use jottings if you need to.

1. Here are the prices at the café.

menu	
burger	82p
egg	37p
chips	53p
mash	45p
juice	34p
milk	28p

   a Hannah buys egg and chips. How much does she pay?

   b Nicole buys burger and mash. How much does she pay?

   c How much more is a burger than an egg?

   d What does it cost for a burger and chips?

   e What does it cost for an egg and mash?

   f What is the difference in price between chips and mash?

   g Bradley buys a burger. How much change from a pound does he get?

   h What do you pay for two glasses of milk?

   i Jenny wants a burger and some juice. What will it cost her?

   j Anil buys an egg and some juice. What change does he get from a pound?

TASK 3: Missing number sums

 Points to remember

- ⊙ Adding is the inverse of subtracting.
- ⊙ Multiplying is the inverse of dividing.
- ⊙ To solve 'missing number' problems, use a number line.

Do these **without a calculator**.

1. Rebecca thinks of a number.
   She adds 15 and gets 42.

   What is Rebecca's number?

2. Jo thinks of a number.
   She subtracts 32 and gets 46.

   What is Jo's number?

3. Rebecca thinks of another number.
   She takes it away from 73 and gets 39.

   What is Rebecca's number?

4. Copy and complete:

   a $23 + \square = 78$

   b $\square + 29 = 51$

   c $68 + \square = 95$

   d $82 - \square = 55$

   e $\square - 34 = 47$

   f $48 - \square = 29$

TASK 4: Introducing thousands

Points to remember

⊙ A four-digit whole number can be written as thousands, hundreds, tens and units, e.g.
$$7853 = 7000 + 800 + 50 + 3$$

⊙ To put numbers in order, look at the digits from the left.

1 Use each digit once.

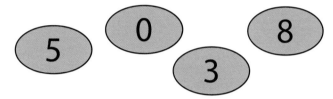

Make the smallest possible number.

2 Use each digit once.

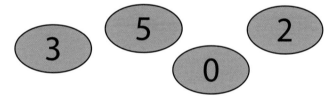

Make the biggest possible number.

3 Write in figures:

   a five thousand, three hundred and twenty-four

   b eight thousand, four hundred and seven

   c three thousand and forty-eight

   d two thousand and sixty

4 Write in words:

   a 6248   **b** 4081   **c** 2103

TASK 5: Multiplying and dividing by 10 or 100

Points to remember

- When a number is:
  - multiplied by 10, its digits move 1 place to the left;
  - multiplied by 100, its digits move 2 places to the left.
- When a number is:
  - divided by 10, the digits move 1 place to the right;
  - divided by 100, the digits move 2 places to the right.

1 How much altogether?

   a ten 5p coins   **b** ten 20p coins   **c** one hundred 50p coins

2 This diagram can help you to convert lengths.

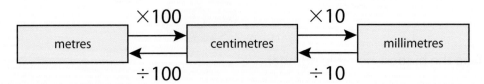

To change metres to centimetres, multiply by 100.
To change centimetres to millimetres, multiply by 10.

To change millimetres to centimetres, divide by 10.
To change centimetres to metres, divide by 100.

Change these to metres.
   a 920 cm   **b** 7500 cm

3 Change these to millimetres.
   a 40 cm   **b** 125 cm

4 Change these to centimetres.
   a 6 m   **b** 20 m   **c** 30 mm   **d** 560 mm

TASK 6: Working out new facts

 Points to remember

⊙ You can work out new facts by:
- using facts you already know;
- using patterns;
- using inverse operations.

Do these without a calculator.

1. Write the answers.

   a 70 × 2 = ...   b 160 ÷ 2 = ...
   c 80 × 5 = ...   d 350 ÷ 5 = ...

2. Use only these numbers.

   30   60   150

   Copy and complete:

   a ... × 2 = ...   b ... ÷ 2 = ...
   c ... × 5 = ...   d ... ÷ 5 = ...

3. Now use only these numbers.

   60   150   300

   Copy and complete:

   a ... × 2 = ...   b ... ÷ 2 = ...
   c ... × 5 = ...   d ... ÷ 5 = ...

TASK 7: Sevens and nines

You may **use your calculator**.

1 A can of cola costs 90p. A can of water costs 70p.

What do these cost?

a 6 cans of water

b 4 cans of cola

c 2 cans of water and 3 cans of cola

d 3 cans of water and 2 cans of cola

e 5 cans of water and 5 cans of cola

f 6 cans of water and 8 cans of cola

g 7 cans of water and 9 cans of cola

2 John buys 10 cans of water and 10 cans of cola.
How much change does he get from £20?

TASK 8: Puzzles

1. Adam has 20 silver coins.
   He puts them all in piles.

   Some piles have 7 coins.
   The rest have 2 coins.

   How many piles of coins has Adam made?

2. Sarah has less than 50 CDs.

   She counted her CDs in sixes.
   She had 4 left over.

   She counted them in fives.
   She had 2 left over.

   How many CDs does Sarah have?

TASK 1: Reading time

Points to remember

⊙ There are 60 minutes in an hour.

⊙ The numbers on the clock face show the hours.

⊙ They have a different value when the minute hand is pointing to them.

1 What time do these four clocks show?

a

b

c

d

2 Write these times in digital clock form.

   a 4 o'clock   **b** quarter past 5   **c** twenty to 1

   d ten past 7   **e** half past 11   **f** quarter to 8

   g five past 3   **h** twenty five past 1   **i** five to 9

   j ten to 2   **k** 25 to 10

TASK 2: A long time

Points to remember

⊙ To work out a time interval, count on from the start time.

⊙ A blank time line helps you to work out a time interval.

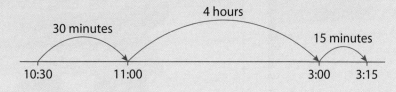

1. Write how long it is between:
   a 4:15 and 5:15
   b 3:25 and 5:15
   c 1:05 and 3:35
   d 7:55 and 9:10
   e 6:35 and 8:15

2. The school bus leaves St Cleer at 2:10.
   It arrives in Bodmin at 2:55.

   How long is the journey?

3. *Big Brother* starts at 10:35.
   It lasts for 1 hour 35 minutes.

   At what time does it finish?

4. Tea time is at 4:45.
   The cake for tea takes 1 hour 20 minutes
   to cook.

   At what time must it go in the oven?

TASK 3: Choosing units of length

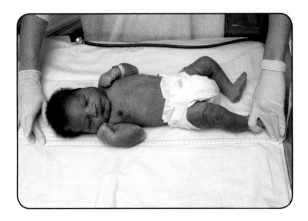 

Points to remember

⊙ Use millimetres (mm) for very small distances, e.g. the length of an ant.

⊙ Use centimetres (cm) for small distances, e.g. the length of a book.

⊙ Use metres (m) for longer distances, e.g. the length of the school hall.

⊙ Use kilometres (km) for very long distances, e.g. the length of a river.

1. What unit would you use to measure these?

   Write **millimetre**, **centimetre**, **metre** or **kilometre**.

   a The length of a new born baby

   b The height of your school

   c The distance from Paris to Sydney

   d The width of a pencil

   e The length of a pencil

   f The width of your bedroom

   g The height of a television

   h The distance around the Earth

   i The distance around a tree trunk

   j The distance from your house to school

   k The length of a flea

TASK 4: The metric system

⊙ Points to remember

⊙ This chart will help you to change one unit of length to another.

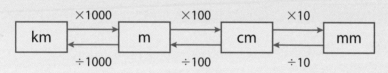

You may **use your calculator**.

1 How many millimetres is 12 cm?

2 Change these to centimetres.

    a 230 mm

    b 6 m

    c 2 m 80 cm

3 Change these to metres.

    a 200 cm

    b 9 km

    c 1 km 300 m

TASK 5: Measuring length

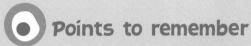

Points to remember

⊙ When you use a ruler to measure or draw lines, position the zero mark on the ruler at the end of the line.

⊙ Write a length of 2 metres and 80 centimetres as 2 m 80 cm.

1 Measure the length of each pencil.

a

b

c

d

e

2 What length is shown here?

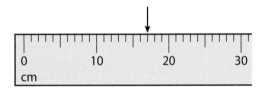

3 What is the height of the table?

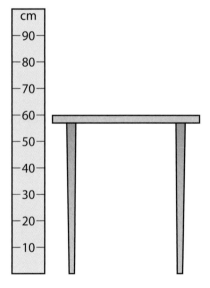

Fractions

$\frac{1}{2}$ of a treacle tart

$\frac{3}{4}$ of a custard pie

$2\frac{1}{4}$ oranges

TASK 1: Fractions of shapes

Points to remember

⊙ A fraction is part of a whole.

⊙ If a shape has 3 out of 8 equal parts shaded, then $\frac{3}{8}$ is shaded.

⊙ The top number of a fraction is the **numerator**.

⊙ The bottom number is the **denominator**.

You need squared paper.

1 Draw the shape. Shade the fraction.

a Shade $\frac{1}{4}$.

b Shade $\frac{3}{4}$.

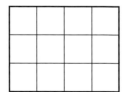

c Shade $\frac{1}{2}$.

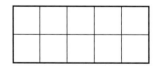

d Shade $\frac{1}{5}$.

e Shade $\frac{2}{3}$.

f Shade $\frac{5}{6}$.

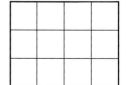

TASK 2: Fractions of numbers

● Points to remember

⊙ Find fractions by dividing.
⊙ To find $\frac{1}{3}$, divide by 3.
⊙ To find $\frac{1}{4}$, divide by 4, or find half of one half.
⊙ To find three quarters, work out one quarter, then multiply by 3.

1 What fraction is shaded?

a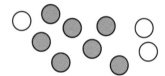

b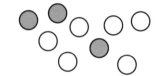

2 Work these out. Show your working.

   a $\frac{1}{10}$ of 90   **b** $\frac{1}{8}$ of 24   **c** $\frac{1}{3}$ of 15   **d** $\frac{1}{100}$ of 300

3 Peter has saved £80.
He spends $\frac{1}{10}$ of it on a canoe ride.
How much does his ride cost?

4 $\frac{3}{4}$ of the 28 pupils in a class like pears.
How many of the pupils like pears?

TASK 3: Comparing fractions

 Points to remember

⊙ **Equivalent fractions** are the same as each other.

⊙ Use diagrams to compare fractions.

Use this fraction wall.

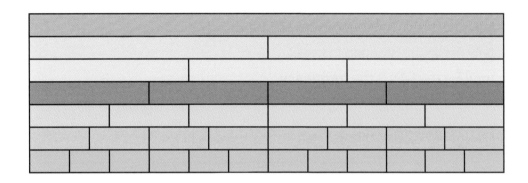

1. Which fraction is bigger?

   a $\frac{1}{4}$ or $\frac{1}{3}$

   b $\frac{1}{8}$ or $\frac{1}{12}$

   c $\frac{1}{6}$ or $\frac{1}{8}$

   d $\frac{1}{2}$ or $\frac{2}{3}$

   e $\frac{3}{4}$ or $\frac{2}{3}$

   f $\frac{5}{6}$ or $\frac{7}{8}$

2. Copy and complete these.

   a $\frac{6}{12} = \frac{\square}{2}$

   b $\frac{2}{8} = \frac{\square}{4}$

   c $\frac{8}{12} = \frac{\square}{3}$

   d $\frac{6}{8} = \frac{\square}{4}$

   e $\frac{9}{12} = \frac{\square}{4}$

   f $1 = \frac{\square}{6}$

Graphs and charts 2

TASK 1: Tally charts and frequency tables

● Points to remember

⊙ In a tally chart each mark stands for one item.

⊙ The tally marks are grouped in fives.

⊙ The total for the tally is the **frequency**.

① Ellie threw a dice 40 times. The tally chart shows her results.

Score	Tally	Frequency
1	IIII	
2	ⅢⅢ III	
3	ⅢⅢ I	
4	ⅢⅢ II	
5	ⅢⅢ IIII	
6	ⅢⅢ I	

a Which score came up the most often?

b Which score came up least often?

c How many more times did 2 come up than 6?

② Harry throws a dice 20 times. Here are his scores.

 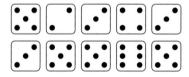

a Make a tally chart for Harry's scores like the one in question 1.
Complete the frequency column.

b Which score came up the most often?

c Which came up the least often?

TASK 2: Bar charts

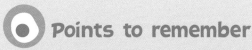

Points to remember

- A **bar chart** helps you to compare data. Important things to look for are:
  - the tallest bar;
  - the shortest bar.
- When you compare charts, look for things that are the same or different.

1 This bar chart shows the different types of clothing that a shop sold in a week:

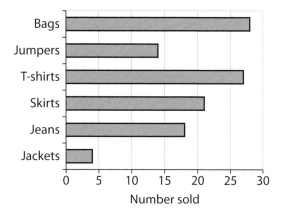

a Write two sentences about what the bar chart shows.

b Estimate how many more T-shirts were sold than skirts.

2 These bar charts show the clothing that a shop sold in January and July.

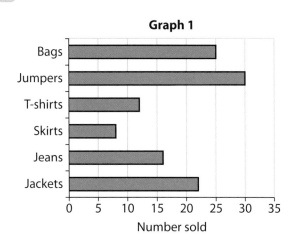

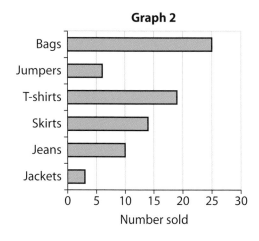

a Which graph do you think is for January? Why?

b Which graph do you think is for July? Why?

TASK 3: Pictograms

Points to remember

- You can use a **pictogram** to represent data.
- A **key** should show how many items each symbol stands for.
- A symbol can represent more than one item.
- The symbols should be the same size.
- The symbols should line up neatly.

1 Nick took part in six sporting events.

This pictogram shows his scores.

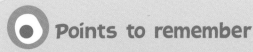

Event

swimming	⬤ ⬤ ⬤
cycling	⬤ ◖
running	⬤ ⬤ ⬤ ◖
high jump	⬤ ◖
shot putt	
javelin	⬤ ⬤

Key: ⬤ stands for 2 points

a Which was Nick's best event?

b Which was Nick's worst event?

c In which events did Nick score 3 points?

d In which events did Nick score more than 5 points?

e How many more points did Nick score for swimming than for the javelin?

f How many points did Nick score altogether?

TASK 4: Carroll diagrams

1. These shapes are lettered from A to K.

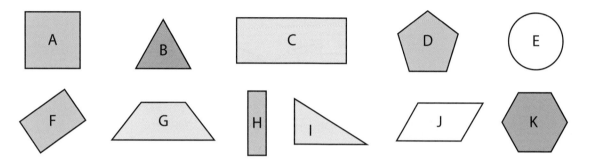

a. Draw this Carroll diagram.

has four sides	does not have four sides

b. Write the letters for shapes A to K in the correct places on your Carroll diagram.

c. Now draw this Carroll diagram.

	has four sides	does not have four sides
Orange		
Not orange		

d. Write the letters for shapes A to K in the correct places on your Carroll diagram.

TASK 5: Venn diagrams

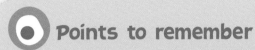

⊙ Points to remember

⊙ A **Venn diagram** is useful for sorting information.

⊙ Data can go inside or outside the circles depending on its properties.

1. This Venn diagram shows some children's names.

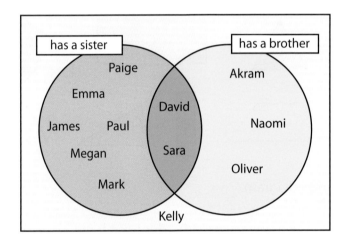

a **Which children have a brother and a sister?**

b **Who has no brothers or sisters?**

c **How many children have a sister but no brother?**

2. Draw this Venn diagram. Label the circle 'Ten times table'.

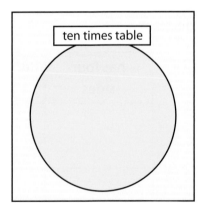

Write each of these numbers in the correct place on your Venn diagram.

20,   31,   46,   50,   90,   67,   45,   78,   10,   21

Money and decimals

TASK 1: Coins and notes

 Points to remember

⊙ To find the total value of several coins, group the coins. Start with the coins with the biggest value.

⊙ To find change from £1, count up to the next multiple of 10p, and then on to 100p.

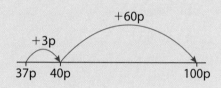

(1) Write your change from £1 when you pay:

  a 53p **b** 38p **c** 17p **d** 64p **e** 88p

(2) Draw a blank 3 by 3 grid. This is your stamp card.

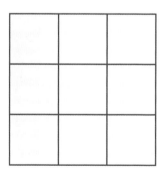

Imagine you have three 5p stamps, three 10p stamps and three 15p stamps.

| 5p | 5p | 5p | 10p | 10p | 10p | 15p | 15p | 15p |

One stamp must go in each space on the card.
The total value of each row, column and diagonal must be 30p.
Write the values of the stamps in the spaces on the card.

TASK 2: Pounds and pence

 Points to remember

- There are 100 pence in £1.
- £4.67 means 4 pounds and 67 pence.
- The two ways to write 35 pence are 35p or £0.35.
- To change pounds to pence, write the digits without a point.
- To change pence to pounds, make the last two digits the pence.
- To add or subtract pounds and pence, write them in columns.
  Line up the points under each other.

1. Write these in pence.

   a £2.50   b £4.20   c £7.00

   d £0.45   e £0.03   f £0.80

2. Write these in pounds.

   a 539p   b 65p   c 350p

   d 600p   e 2p   f 40p

3. Work these out **without a calculator**.
   Show your working.

   a £4.35 + 87p

   b £5.48 + 23p

   c £3.74 + £1.58

   d £13.67 − £4.25

TASK 3: Money problems

Points to remember

⊙ Read problems carefully.

⊙ Change different units to the same unit.

⊙ Decide what sum to do and write it down.

⊙ Decide whether to do the sum in your head, on paper or using a calculator.

⊙ When you use a calculator, think how to interpret the display.

⊙ If you make a mistake using a calculator, press ON and start again.

⊙ Check the answer makes sense.

⊙ Include units in the answer.

You may **use your calculator**.

1   Here are the prices at the shoe shop.

Trainers	£32.67	Boots	£34.72
Sandals	£24.33	Slip-ons	£29.34
High heels	£41.28	Lace ups	£26.67
Laces	87p	Tin of polish	78p

a   Dylan buys some trainers and a pair of boots.
    How much does he pay?

b   Amy buys slip-ons and high heels.
    How much change does she get from £80?

c   Kieran buys two pairs of sandals and some polish.
    What does it cost him altogether?

d   How much more are slip-ons than lace ups?

e   Connor spends £6.09 on laces. How many sets of laces does he buy?

f   How many tins of polish can you buy for £5? How much change will you get?

g   Imogen has £90. She buys two pairs of sandals. Can she afford the high heels?

TASK 4: Tenths

 Points to remember

⊙ 0.1 means one tenth or $\frac{1}{10}$.

⊙ 0.5 means five tenths or $\frac{5}{10}$, which is the same as $\frac{1}{2}$.

⊙ 3.7 means 3 ones and 7 tenths. You can write 3.7 as 3 + 0.7, or 3 + $\frac{7}{10}$.

⊙ The decimal point separates the whole number from the part less than 1.

① Write the number that each arrow is pointing to.

a

b

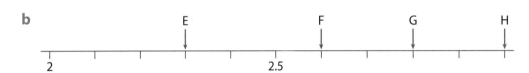

c

② Write in centimetres (cm) the length of the pencil.

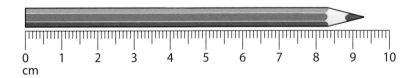

③ Write in kilograms (kg) the weight of each parcel.

a 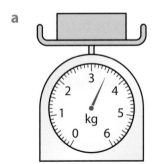 **b** 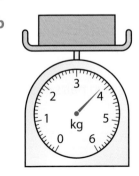 **c**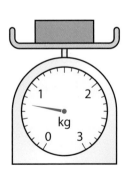

TASK 5: Tenths and hundredths

Did you know that...?

Russia was the first country in the world to have a **decimal currency**.

In 1710, Peter the Great made the Russian rouble equal to 100 kopecks.

Points to remember

⊙ The decimal point separates the whole number from the part less than 1.

⊙ Each digit in a decimal has a place value.

⊙ The first decimal place is for tenths and the second decimal place is for hundredths.

 Write the value of the **9** in each of these.

    a £58.**9**3   b £**9**18.6   c £1.6**9**   d £**9**2.7   e £0.**9**3

② Write the answers.

    a 6p more than £3.78   b 5p less than £4.23

    c 4p more than £5.99   d 9p less than £3.05

③ Copy and complete each sequence.

    a £2.37, £2.38, £2.39, ..., ..., ...

    b £9.53, £9.52, £9.51, ..., ..., ...

    c £8.34, £8.24, £8.14, ..., ..., ...

    d £3.06, £3.04, £3.02, ..., ..., ...

Measures 2

TASK 1: Clocks and timetables

◉ Points to remember

- ⊙ Use **am** to show times in the morning before 12 noon, or midday.
- ⊙ Use **pm** to show times in the afternoon or evening, after midday.
- ⊙ To work out a time interval, count on from the start time to the end time.
- ⊙ You can use a blank time line to help work out time intervals.

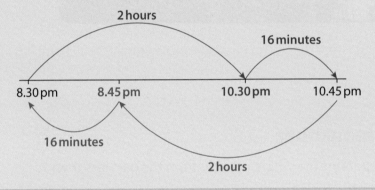

1. Write in digital clock time using am or pm.

   a Quarter past 10 in the morning
   b 10 past 2 in the afternoon
   c Quarter to 4 in the afternoon
   d 20 to 6 in the morning

2. Hannah gets up for school at 7:35 am. She leaves home 45 minutes later. Her journey takes 15 minutes. What time does she get to school?

3. This timetable shows the morning trains from Carlisle to Euston (London).

Carlisle	7:15 am	8:20 am	9:35 am	10:50 am	11:35 am
Euston	11:30 am	12:30 pm	1:30 pm	2:05 pm	3:30 pm

   a How long does each journey take?

   b What time does the fastest train leave Carlisle?

   c Mr Callow has a meeting in London at 2:15 pm.
      His meeting is a 30-minute walk away from Euston Station.
      Which train should Mr Callow catch in Carlisle?

TASK 2: Seconds, minutes, hours, days, weeks

 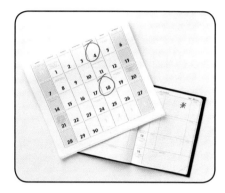 

 Points to remember

There are:

- ⊙ 60 seconds in 1 minute;
- ⊙ 60 minutes in 1 hour;
- ⊙ 24 hours in 1 day;
- ⊙ 7 days in 1 week.

You may **use your calculator**.

1. Change these times into seconds.
   - a 6 minutes
   - b 12 minutes
   - c 5 minutes and 10 seconds

2. Change these times into minutes.
   - a 4 hours
   - b 7 hours
   - c 6 hours and 40 minutes

3. Change these times into hours.
   - a 2 days
   - b 120 minutes

TASK 3: Scales

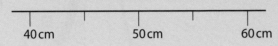
1 Here is part of a ruler marked in centimetres.
Write the measurements shown by the arrows **a**, **b** and **c**.

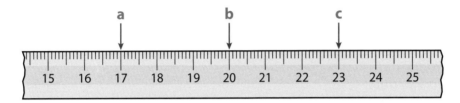

2 What is the length of each pencil? Write your answer in centimetres and millimetres.

a
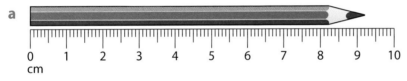

b

c
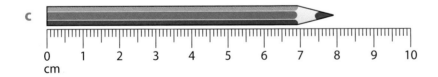

3 What number is each pointer pointing to?

a
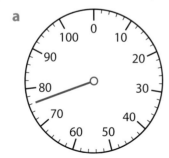

b
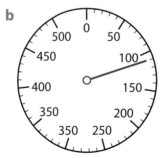

c
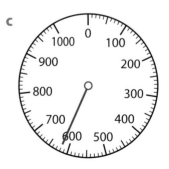

TASK 4: Mass

Points to remember

⊙ There are 1000 grams in 1 kilogram.

⊙ Lighter objects are measured using grams (g).

⊙ Heavier objects are measured using kilograms (kg).

⊙ 'Kilo' means one thousand.

① Copy and complete each sentence by choosing one of the weights.

a The weight of an egg is about ...... g.

   5 g   50 g   500 g   5000 g

b The weight of a large loaf of bread is about ...... g.

   8 g   80 g   800 g   8000 g

c The weight of a bunch of bananas is about ...... g.

   2 g   20 g   200 g   2000 g

② Write whether you would weigh these using grams (g) or kilograms (kg).

a a packet of butter

b a sack of potatoes

c a horse

d a mouse

③ What weight is shown on the scales?

a

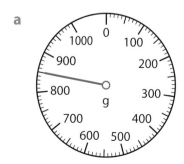

b

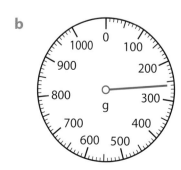

TASK 5: Capacity

Points to remember

- There are 1000 millilitres in 1 litre.
- Smaller capacities are measured using millilitres (ml).
- Larger capacities are measured using litres (l).
- 'Milli' means one thousandth.

1. About how much does a coffee mug hold?
   Choose from:

   30 millilitres   300 millilitres   3 litres   30 litres

2. How much water is there in each measuring cylinder?

a
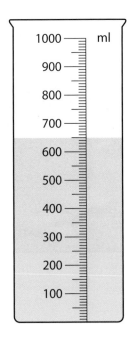

b
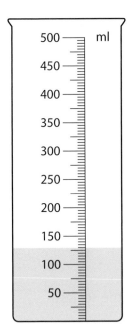

c
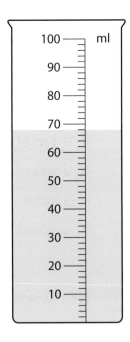

3. A bottle of shampoo holds 500 ml.
   Jemma uses 20 ml each time she washes her hair.

   Jemma washes her hair three times.
   How much shampoo is left in the bottle?

Number and measures

TASK 1: Positive and negative numbers

⦿ Points to remember

- ⊙ −5 is 'negative 5'.
- ⊙ −6°C is minus six degrees Celsius. It is six degrees below zero.
- ⊙ −10°C is a lower temperature than −5°C.
- ⊙ Include the units when you write a temperature.

① **a** The temperature was −4°C.
It went up by 7 degrees.
What was the new temperature?

b The temperature was 5°C.
It fell by 8 degrees.
What was the new temperature?

c In Rome it was 3°C.
In London it was −2°C.
How many degrees colder was it
in London?

② Look at these temperatures.

$$-1°C \quad 4°C \quad 0°C \quad -5°C \quad 3°C$$

Write them in order, coldest first.

③ Use this number line to help you.

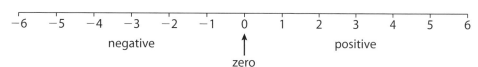

a −4 + 5   **b** −1 + 6   **c** −3 + 2

d 4 − 5   **e** 3 − 9   **f** −6 + 6

TASK 2: Reading scales

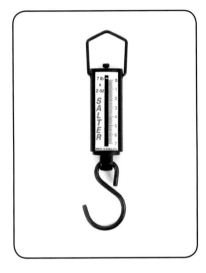  

🎯 Points to remember

⊙ A scale can be horizontal or vertical, or straight or curved.

⊙ To read a scale, first work out the step size.

⊙ Work out the values of the marks close to the pointer.

⊙ If the pointer is between two marks, estimate the reading.

You need a copy of **N1.7 Resource sheet 2.2**.

1 What number is the arrow pointing to on this scale?

2 How much flour is shown on this scale?

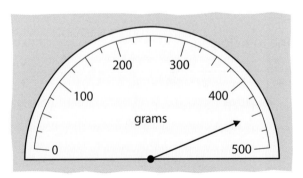

Questions 3, 4 and 5 are on **N1.7 Resource sheet 2.2**.

TASK 3: Adding tenths

 Points to remember

- 0.7 and $\frac{7}{10}$ both mean 7 tenths.
- You can add tenths by counting on in tenths.
- Use an empty number line to help add tenths, e.g. 5.7 + 0.4 = 6.1.

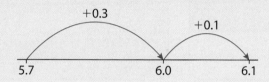

1. Work these out.

   a 0.2 + 0.5   b 0.3 + 0.6   c 1.8 + 0.4   d 4.7 + 0.5

   e 1.3 + 0.8   f 2.9 + 0.3   g 6.1 + 0.7   h 5.8 + 0.2

2. What are these numbers?

   a three tenths more than 1.8   b five tenths less than 4.7

   c four tenths more than 6.9   d one tenth less than 7.0

TASK 4: Tenths and hundredths

 Points to remember

- The first decimal place is for tenths and the second is for hundredths.
- 0.1 is equivalent to $\frac{1}{10}$ and 0.03 is equivalent to $\frac{3}{100}$.
- 0.56 is equivalent to $\frac{56}{100}$.

1. Write as fractions:

   a 0.02   b 0.78   c 0.9   d 0.61   e 2.05

2. Write as decimals:

   a $\frac{8}{100}$ b $\frac{29}{100}$ c $\frac{7}{10}$ d $2\frac{45}{100}$ e $1\frac{8}{100}$

TASK 5: Metres, centimetres and millimetres

 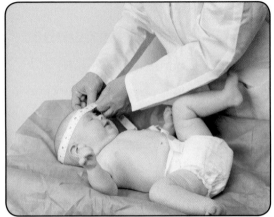

Points to remember

⊙ 1 metre is 100 centimetres.

⊙ 1 centimetre is 10 millimetres.

⊙ You can write 65 cm as 0.65 metres.
465 cm is 4.65 metres.

⊙ You can write 9 mm as 0.9 cm.
29 mm is 2.9 cm.

⊙ When an answer is a measurement, include the units.

① Tim planted some sunflower seeds.

Here are the heights of his sunflowers.
Write them in centimetres.

Plant A	1.27 m	Plant B	2.01 m
Plant C	0.85 m	Plant D	1.6 m

Write the heights of these sunflowers in metres.

Plant E	123 cm	Plant F	204 m
Plant G	90 cm	Plant H	150 m

② Write in millimetres:

   a 2.6 cm   **b** 0.9 cm

③ Write in centimetres:

   a 48 mm   **b** 7 mm

More properties of shapes

TASK 1: Properties of polygons

◉ Points to remember

- You can sort shapes using properties such as:
  - number of sides;
  - number of vertices;
  - number of right angles;
  - number of lines of symmetry;
  - whether the shapes are regular or irregular.
- A **quadrilateral** has four straight sides.

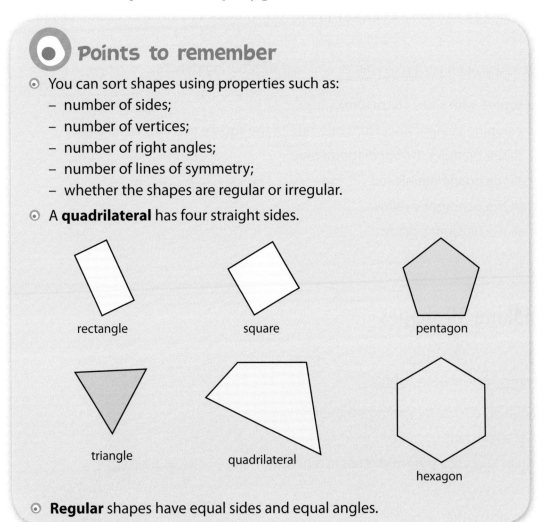

rectangle　　　　square　　　　pentagon

triangle　　　　quadrilateral

hexagon

- **Regular** shapes have equal sides and equal angles.

You will need a piece of scrap paper.

1. What shape is your piece of paper? What properties does it have?

2. Fold in one corner of your paper.
   What shape is your piece of paper now? What properties does this shape have?

3. Fold your paper again so that it makes a shape with three sides.
   What name does this shape have?

4. Fold your paper to make a shape of your own. What is its name?

TASK 2: Making 2D shapes and patterns

⊙ Points to remember

- A **tessellation** is a repeating pattern of shapes with no gaps or overlaps.
- You can make new shapes by:
  - fitting together shapes with equal sides;
  - cutting across a shape with a straight line.

You will need a ruler, a piece of plain paper and some colouring pencils.

1. Draw a square with sides 15 cm long.

   Draw six sloping straight lines from one side of the square to a different side.

   Colour all the triangles in your diagram blue.

   Colour all the quadrilaterals red.

   Colour all the pentagons yellow.

   Colour all the hexagons green.

TASK 3: Making 3D shapes

⊙ Points to remember

- You can build 3D shapes by joining other 3D shapes.
- A **prism** has a constant cross-section.
- The triangular faces of a **pyramid** meet at a point.

You need an empty packet or box and some scissors. You could use a cereal box or a chocolate box.

1. a What shape is the box?

   b Cut the box along its edges so that it opens out flat. Sketch the flat shape.

   c Write the names of the shapes that the flat shape is made of.

TASK 4: Angle

Windmill

Ship's wheel

Wind vane

Points to remember

- Angle is a measure of turn.
- Angles are measured in degrees.
- The symbol ° stands for degrees.
- There are 360° in a whole turn and 180° in a half turn.

You will need a piece of paper, a ruler and some sticky tape or glue.

1. **a** Draw three angles that are less than a right angle.

    b Now draw three angles that are more than a right angle.

    c Cut out your six angles.

    Stick them in your book in order of size, starting with the smallest.

TASK 5: Using the eight compass points

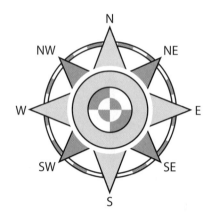

Points to remember

⊙ Compass points are used to give directions.

⊙ The eight main compass points are north, east, south and west, north-east, south-east, south-west and north-west.

Use the map to answer the questions.

1. **a** Which city is south of London?
   b Which city is south-west of Coventry?
   c Which city is west of Sheffield?
   d What direction is Newcastle from Carlisle?
   e What direction is Liverpool from Carlisle?
   f What direction is Liverpool from Coventry?

2. Write two more questions of your own, with answers.

TASK 6: Coordinates

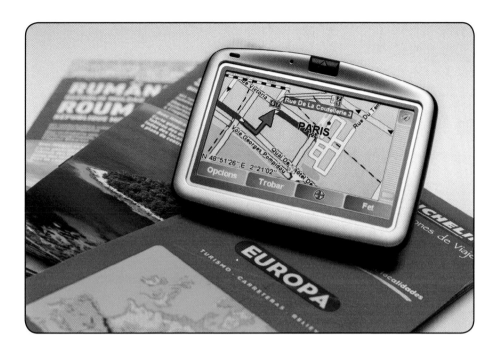

⊙ Points to remember

- ⊙ **Coordinates** describe where a point is on a grid.
- ⊙ Number both axes.
- ⊙ Label the grid lines not the spaces.
- ⊙ To plot coordinates, go across first and then up.
- ⊙ (4, 6) means 4 steps across and 6 steps up.

You will need some squared paper, a ruler and a pencil.

1. Make a copy of this grid.
   Join each set of points in order:
   a   (2, 1), (6, 1), (7, 2), (1, 2)
   b   (6, 2), (6, 5), (4, 3), (6, 3)
   c   (3, 2), (3, 8), (2, 7), (3, 7), (1, 3), (3, 3)

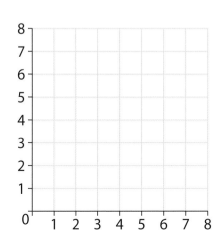

Multiplying and dividing 2

TASK 1: Tables to 10

> **Points to remember**
>
> ⊙ Use facts that you know to work out facts you forget.
> ⊙ To multiply a number by 9, multiply it by 10 and subtract the number.
> ⊙ To multiply a number by 11, multiply if by 10 and add the number.
> ⊙ To multiply by 8, multiply by 4 and double.

1. Draw two 3 by 3 grids.

   Write the numbers 1 to 9, in any order, in one of the grids. For example:

   Write the answers for the **7 times table** in the right place in the other grid.

3	9	7
4	8	2
6	1	5

   $\times 7$

   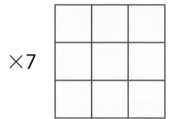

2. Do it again, this time for the **8 times table**.

TASK 2: Multiplying by multiples of 10 or 100

> **Points to remember**
>
> ⊙ When a number is:
>   × 10, its digits move 1 place to the left;
>   × 100, its digits move 2 places to the left.
> ⊙ When a number is:
>   ÷ 10, the digits move 1 place to the right;
>   ÷ 100, the digits move 2 places to the right.
> ⊙ To multiply by 70, multiply by 7, then multiply by 10.
> ⊙ To multiply by 700, multiply by 7, then multiply by 100.

1. Draw two 5 by 2 grids.

   Write the numbers 0 to 9, in any order, in one of the grids. For example:

4	9	5	7	2
0	8	1	3	6

   Multiply each number by 20. Write the answer in the right place in the other grid.

   ×20

2. Do it again, this time multiplying by 500.

TASK 3: Recognising multiples

Points to remember

- A **multiple** of a number divides exactly by the number.
- Multiples of 10 end in 0; multiples of 100 end in 00.
- Multiples of 5 end in 5 or 0; multiples of 50 end in 50 or 00.

1. Write all the numbers in this list that are multiples of 5.

   84   85   86   98   99   100   105   106   107

2. a Write a number that is a multiple of 8.

   b Write a number that is not a multiple of 8.

3. Jin thinks of a number.

   His number is less than 20.
   His number is a multiple of 3.
   His number is a multiple of 4.

   What is Jin's number?

4. Choose three numbers from this list.
   The numbers must add up to a multiple of 10.

   11   12   13   14   15   16   17   18   19

TASK 4: Multiplication

 Points to remember

- Read word problems carefully.
- Decide what calculation to do and write it down.
- Estimate the answer.
- Use a grid to multiply, or a calculator for bigger numbers.
- Show your working.
- Check that the answer is about the right size.
- Include any units in the answer.

1. Work these out **without a calculator**. Show your working.

   a 43×5 b 38×3

   c 74×2 d 126×4

2. **Use a calculator**.

   a A crate holds 36 cans.
   How many cans will 16 crates hold?

   b 12 adults and 4 children went to
   a Safari Park.

   Each adult paid £22.
   Each child paid £16.

   How much did they pay altogether?

   c Apples cost 28p each.
   Oranges cost 36p each.

   What is the total cost of 7 apples
   and 9 oranges?

TASK 5: Division

 Points to remember

- Read word problems carefully.
- Decide what calculation to do and write it down.
- Estimate the answer.
- Use 'chunking' to divide, or a calculator for bigger numbers.
- Show your working.
- Check that the answer is about the right size.
- If necessary, decide whether to round the answer up or down.
- Include any units in the answer.

1 Work these out **without a calculator**. Show your working.

   a 87 ÷ 3   **b** 84 ÷ 4

   c 136 ÷ 4   **d** 185 ÷ 5

2 **Use a calculator.**

   a A box of 8 DVDs costs £100.
      Find the cost of one DVD.

   b Five people have a meal in a restaurant.
      The bill comes to £119.

      They share the cost equally.
      How much does each person pay?

   c Zoe packs games into boxes.
      Each box holds 8 games.

      Zoe has 150 games to pack.
      How many boxes will she need?

Graphs and charts 3

TASK 1: Lists and tables

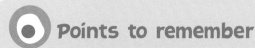
Points to remember

⊙ **Lists and tables** show data in a variety of ways. They help you to:
  – compare information;
  – look for things that are the same or different;
  – look for patterns.

(1) This is the medal table for the 2004 Olympic Games in Athens.

Position	Country	Gold	Silver	Bronze
1	USA	36	39	27
2	China	32	17	14
3	Russia	27	27	38
4	Australia	17	16	16
5	Japan	16	9	12
6	Germany	13	16	20
7	France	11	9	13
8	Italy	10	11	11
9	South Korea	9	12	9
10	Great Britain	9	9	12

a Which country won 10 gold medals?

b Which country won 2 more gold medals than Great Britain?

c How many medals did Japan win altogether?

d Which country won the most silver medals?

e Which country won the most bronze medals?

f Which country came fourth in the medal table?

TASK 2: More lists and tables

Points to remember

⊙ A calendar is a kind of table.

⊙ Tables can show different kinds of information for different purposes.

1 There are lots of different things to do at an outdoor centre.

Activity	Age range (years)	Price
climbing	12–15	£8
canoeing	7–10	£12
cycling	9–12	£8
river trip	12+	£20
high wires	14 +	£18

a Finley is 9 years old.

Write a list of all the activities that he can do.

b Finley's sister is 7 years old.

Write a list of all the activities that she can do.

c What activities can Finley and his sister do together?

d Which activity costs the most?

e Megan has £10. What activities can she afford?

TASK 3: Bar charts

> ### Points to remember
>
> ⊙ A bar chart must have a title.
> ⊙ The axes must have labels.
> ⊙ Leave equal gaps between the bars.
> ⊙ Choose the scale for the frequency axis carefully.
> ⊙ Number the grid lines, not the spaces.

You will need squared paper, a ruler and a pencil.

1. Sophie went pond dipping.

   This table shows the creatures she found.

Type of creature	Frequency
fish	5
pond snail	8
frog	2
dragonfly	1
beetle	11

   a Draw a bar chart to show the information in the table.

   Space the bars at 1 cm intervals.

   Use a vertical scale numbered in 2s.

   b Copy and complete this sentence.

   Sophie found .... creatures altogether.

TASK 4: Interpreting pictograms

Points to remember

⊙ A **pictogram** uses symbols to represent data.

⊙ A **key** shows how many items of data each symbol stands for.

⊙ A symbol can stand for more than one item of data.

⊙ The symbols are the same size and line up neatly.

1. The pupils in Class 7 said which pets they had.

Pets	
hamster	
rabbit	
dog	
cat	
fish	
none	

Key: ▤ stands for 3 pupils

a One pupil has a fish and two people have hamsters.

Write two more sentences about what the pictogram shows.

b How many more pupils had cats than hamsters?

c How many dogs and cats altogether are owned by the pupils in Class 7?

TASK 5: Drawing pictograms

1. Some pupils said what they spent their pocket money on.

Item	Number of pupils
sweets	12
cinema	4
clothes	9
magazines	7
savings	3
going out	14

a Draw a pictogram to show this data.

Choose a symbol to stand for two pupils.

b What did most pupils spend their money on?

c What did fewest pupils spend their money on?

TASK 6: Venn and Carroll diagrams

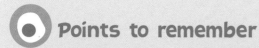

Points to remember

⊙ **Venn and Carroll diagrams** are for sorting data.

⊙ All the data fits in each diagram.

⊙ A two-way Carroll diagram has two rows and two columns.

⊙ A two-way Venn diagram has two overlapping circles:
  – data in the overlap has both properties;
  – data outside both circles does not have either of the properties.

1 This table shows some pupils' names, ages and hair colour.

Name	Age	Hair colour
Ellie	12	brown
Clare	13	blonde
Rhys	13	black
Lewis	12	blonde
Lauren	14	brown
Mark	13	brown

a Copy this Venn diagram.
Write the names in the right places.

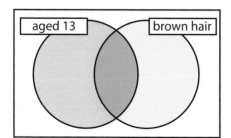

b Copy this Carroll diagram.
Write the names in the right places.

	aged 13	not aged 13
brown hair		
not brown hair		

TASK 1: Clocks, timetables and calendars

⦿ Points to remember

⊙ There are 52 weeks in one year.

⊙ A normal year has 365 days.

⊙ Every fourth year is a leap year.
A leap year has an extra day in February.

⊙ Some months have 31 days and some have 30 days. February has 28 or 29 days.

60 seconds	= 1 minute
60 minutes	= 1 hour
24 hours	= 1 day
7 days	= 1 week
12 months	= 1 year

1   Here is the calendar for December 2010.

DECEMBER						
Sun	Mon	Tues	Wed	Thu	Fri	Sat
			1	2	3	4
5	6	7	8	9	10	11
12	13	14	15	16	17	18
19	20	21	22	23	24	25
26	27	28	29	30	31	

a   What day is Christmas Day (25th December)?

b   Jennifer's birthday is six days before Christmas Day.
What day and date is this?

c   Matthew's birthday is four days after Christmas Day.
What day and date is this?

d   Hanukkah is on Thursday 2nd December in 2010.
How many days before Christmas Day is Hanukkah?

e   The Muslim New Year, Al-Hijra, is on 7th December in 2010.
How many days before 1st January 2011 is this?

TASK 2: Reading more scales

Points to remember

- Look carefully at a scale to work out the step size.
- Work out the values of the marks close to the pointer.
- If the pointer is between two marks, estimate the reading.
- You can use decimals to record measurements.
- On this scale, there are 10 steps between 2 and 3.
  Each step represents one tenth.
  The pointer shows 2.3.

1. Here is a centimetre ruler. What lengths are shown by the arrows A, B, C and D?

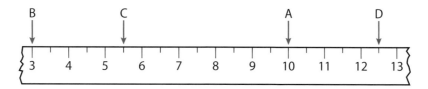

2. Here is a measuring cylinder. What measurements are shown by the arrows A, B, C and D?

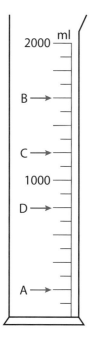

3. Here is a speedometer. What speed is the pointer pointing to?

TASK 3: Standard metric units 1

1   Write the weight shown by each arrow.

2   Write the weight shown by each arrow.

3   Write the weight shown by each arrow.

Task 4: Standard metric units 2

Points to remember

- ⊙ **milli** means one thousandth.
- ⊙ **centi** means one hundredth.
- ⊙ **kilo** means one thousand.

Example

- ◎ 230 cm = 2 m 30 cm = 2.3 m
- ◎ 4600 g = 4 kg 600 g = 4.6 kg
- ◎ 9500 ml = 9 litres 500 ml = 9.5 litres

1. A kettle holds 1.7 litres of water. Copy and complete this sentence:

    1.7 litres is the same as ...... litre ...... millilitres

2. A desk is 120 cm long. Copy and complete this sentence:

    120 cm is the same as ...... metre ...... centimetres

3. A curtain is 1.9 m long. Copy and complete this sentence:

    1.9 m is the same as ...... metre ...... centimetres

4. A bag of potatoes weighs 4500 g. Copy and complete this sentence:

    4500 g is the same as ...... kilograms ...... grams

5. Copy and complete this table. The first row is done for you.

1400 ml	1 litre 400 ml	1.4 litres
730 cm	… m … cm	… m
… g	… kg … g	6.1 kg
… ml	… litres … ml	7.6 litres
… mm	9 cm 4 mm	… cm

Task 5: Perimeter

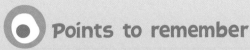

Points to remember

⊙ The **perimeter** is the total distance around the edge of a shape.

⊙ To find the perimeter of a shape, add up the lengths of all the sides.

⊙ Perimeters are measured in units of length such as centimetres.

1) These rectangles are drawn on a centimetre grid. Work out the perimeter of each rectangle.

a   b

c

2) Work out the perimeter of each shape.

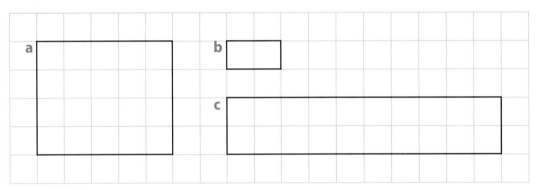

a   8 mm

5 mm   5 mm

8 mm

b   5 cm

5 cm   5 cm

5 cm   5 cm

5 cm

3) This shape is drawn on a centimetre grid.
What is its perimeter?

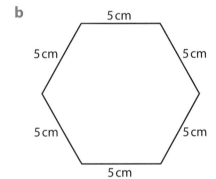

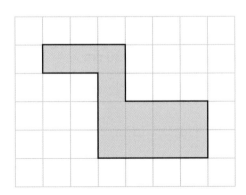

Task 6: Area

Points to remember

- **Area** is a measure of the surface of a shape.
- To find an area, count the number of squares that the shape covers.
- Area is measured in square units such as square centimetres or square metres.

For all of the questions on squared grids each square is 1 square centimetre.

Remember to write cm² at the end of each of your answers.

① These rectangles are drawn on a centimetre grid. Work out the area of each rectangle.

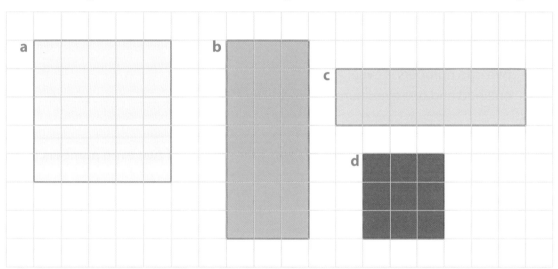

② These shapes are drawn on a centimetre grid. Work out the area of each shape.

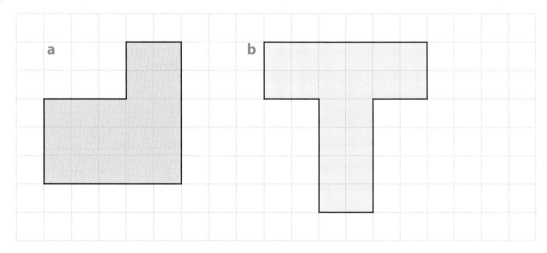

③ On squared paper draw a rectangle that has an area of 18 squares.

Solving number problems

TASK 1: Odd and even numbers

Points to remember

- The **sum** of:
  - two even numbers is even;
  - two odd numbers is even;
  - one odd and one even number is odd.
- The **difference** of:
  - two even numbers is even;
  - two odd numbers is even;
  - one odd and one even number is odd.

① Write four different examples to show that the sum of two even numbers is even.

② Write four different examples to show that the difference of two even numbers is even.

③ Write four different examples to show that the difference of one odd and one even number is odd.

④ Copy this diagram. Write one number in each of the four spaces.

	even	not even
multiple of 5		
not a multiple of 5		

TASK 2: Addition problems

Points to remember

⊙ Make a table to show information.

⊙ List possibilities systematically.

⊙ Check that the solution fits the problem.

(1) A pizza and a pie cost £8 altogether.
A pie and a pudding cost £9 altogether.
A pizza, a pie and a pudding cost £12 altogether.

How much does the pizza cost?

How much does the pie cost?

How much does the pudding cost?

TASK 3: Using clues

Points to remember

⊙ Think about the order in which to use the clues.

⊙ List possibilities systematically.

⊙ Check that the solution fits the problem.

(1) Amber's number is a two-digit odd number.
It is less than 60.
One digit is double the other.

What is Amber's number?

(2) Kyle's number is a two-digit multiple of 5.
It is more than 50.
The difference between the digits is 1.

What is Kyle's number?

(3) Ella's two-digit number is less than 60.
The sum of the digits is 12.
The difference between the digits is 2.

What is Ella's number?

TASK 4: Working systematically 1

1. Here is a sequence of shapes made with blue and grey tiles.
   The sequence goes on in the same way.

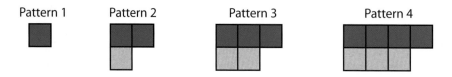

Pattern 1   Pattern 2   Pattern 3   Pattern 4

a Copy and complete this table.

Pattern number	1	2	3	4	5	6
Number of blue tiles						
Number of grey tiles						
Total number of tiles						

b Altogether, how many tiles will be in pattern 10?

c Altogether, how many tiles will be in pattern 100?

TASK 5: Working systematically 2

Points to remember

⊙ Count possibilities systematically.

⊙ It may help to make a list or table.

⊙ Check that the solution works.

1   2   3   4   5   6

① Write the numbers **1, 2, 3, 4, 5** and **6** on scraps of paper.

Arrange them in a triangle.

Make each side of the triangle add up to **12**.

Now draw the triangle with the numbers in your book.

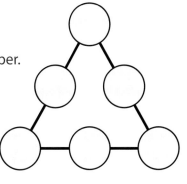

Revision unit 1

TASK 1: Place value

> ### ⊙ Points to remember
> - ⊙ You can partition numbers like this: 7824 = 7000 + 800 + 20 + 4.
> - ⊙ To order numbers, look at the values of the digits, starting from the left.
> - ⊙ Round up fives, e.g. 45 rounds to 50.

1 *2006 Progress Test level 3*

In the number 4378, the figure 7 represents 7 tens.

a What does the figure 3 represent?

b What does the figure 4 represent?

c Write in figures the number **twenty thousand and twenty**.

2 *2003 KS2 level 3*

Write these numbers in order of size, starting with the smallest.

164   146   106   160   140

3 *2004 KS2 level 3*

Which of these numbers is closest to 700?

750   72   651   69   770

4 *2004 KS2 level 3*

Katie has these digit cards. She makes different two-digit numbers with them.

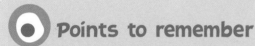

Write all the two-digit numbers Katie can make with them.

TASK 2: Adding and subtracting

 Points to remember

- To add or subtract numbers in columns, line up the units under units, the tens under tens, and so on.
- Count up from the smaller to the larger number to subtract, find the difference, or find how many more or how many less.
- To find the sum, add all the numbers.
- To find a difference, take the smaller number from the bigger number.

(1) *2002 level 3*

    a Add together 156 and 417   **b** Subtract 192 from 638

(2) *2003 Progress Test level 3*

Copy and fill in the missing numbers.

    a 36 + ☐ = 100   **b** 100 – ☐ = 51

(3) *2006 Progress Test level 3*

Nisha writes:

$$538 + 46 = 585$$

Show why Nisha is wrong.

(4) *2004 Key Stage 2 level 3*

These are the prices of sandwiches, drinks and fruit.

Sandwiches		Drinks		Fruit	
cheese	£1.45	milk	55p	apple	15p
tuna	£1.70	cola	45p	pear	20p
salad	£1.20	juice	65p	melon	25p

    a Shereen buys a tuna sandwich, milk and a pear.
       How much does she pay?

    b Mike has 80p to spend on a fruit and a drink.
       What two things can he buy for exactly 80p?

TASK 3: Money problems

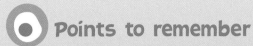

Points to remember

- Decide what calculation to do and write it down.
- Decide whether to use a mental, written or calculator method.
- When you use a calculator, think about how to enter numbers and interpret the display. Jot down answers to interim steps.
- Include the £ or p sign in your final answer.

Do question 1 **without using a calculator**. For question 2, you may **use a calculator**.

1 *2007 Key Stage 2 level 3*

Here are three bags in a shop

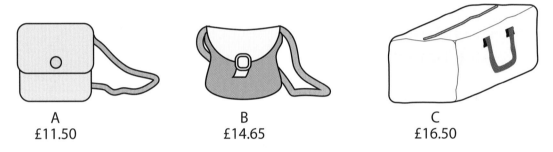

| A | B | C |
| £11.50 | £14.65 | £16.50 |

  a How much does bag B cost to the nearest pound?

  b Jamie buys bag A and bag C. How much change does he get from £40?

2 *1998 Key Stage 2 level 3*

  a 102 people came to a school's car boot sale.

     They paid 15p each to go in.

     How much money was collected at the entrance?

  b Each car had to pay £7 to be at the sale.

     The school collected £399 from the cars.

     How many cars were there?

TASK 4: Properties of shapes

1. *2003 KS2 level 3*

   The letter D has a line of symmetry.

   Which of the other letters have a line of symmetry?

   D   M   E   S   N

2. *1999 level 3*

   Look at these six angles.

   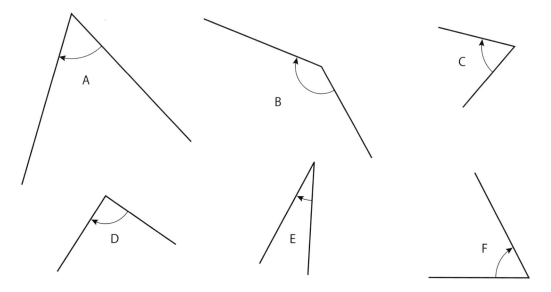

   a   Which is the smallest angle?

   b   Which is the biggest angle?

   c   One of the angles is a right angle. Which is a right angle?

   d   One of the angles is an obtuse angle. Which is an obtuse angle?

TASK 5: Tables, graphs and charts

⊙ Points to remember

- ⊙ Lists and tables allow you to:
  - compare information;
  - look for differences and similarities;
  - look for patterns.
- ⊙ Bar charts help you to spot patterns and to compare sets of data.
- ⊙ The scale on a bar chart helps you to interpret the chart.

(1) *1997 Key Stage 2 level 3*

Here are the times of some television programmes.

Channel 1	
7:00	Cartoon
7:15	Film
9:00	News
9:30	Weather
9:35	Sport
10:20	Drama

Channel 2	
7:00	Local news
7:45	Quiz show
8:30	Comedy
9:00	Hospital drama
10:00	Pop chart
10:40	Film

a What is showing on Channel 2 at ten minutes to eight?

b Tom watches Hospital drama and then changes to Channel 1 at the end.
What is showing on Channel 1 when he changes channel?

c The film on Channel 2 starts at 10.40. It lasts for one and a half hours.
At what time does the film end?

The table shows when Julie has to hand in homework for different subjects.

	Mon	Tue	Wed	Thu	Fri
Maths	✓			✓	
English		✓		✓	
Science			✓		
French	✓		✓		
Technology				✓	
Art					✓
Music		✓			

a On what two days does Julie have to hand in French homework?

b On Thursdays, Julie has to hand in homework for three subjects.
   What subjects are these?

c On Tuesday, the art teacher gives Julie her homework.
   How many nights are there before she has to hand in her art homework?

③ *1999 Key Stage 2 level 3*

These are the times letters are collected from a post box.

Monday to Friday	Saturday	Sunday
8:00 am

2:00 pm

6:30 pm | 11:30 am | no collection |

a What is the latest time letters are collected on Wednesday?

b Carla posts a letter at 9 am on Monday.
   How long will it be before it is collected?

c Gareth posts a letter on Saturday at 3 pm.
   When is it collected from the post box?

Revision unit 2

TASK 1: Sequences

> ### Points to remember
>
> ⊙ A **sequence** of numbers follows a rule.
> ⊙ When a sequence goes up or down in equal steps, you can work out the rule and the next terms.
> ⊙ **Multiples of 3** are numbers that divide exactly by 3.
> ⊙ The rule for the sequence of multiples of 3 is 'add 3'.

(1) *2007 KS2 level 3*

Here is part of a number sequence.
The numbers increase by the same amount each time.

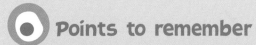

The sequence continues.
Write all of the numbers below that would appear in the sequence.

840   905   989   1000   2051

(2) *1998 KS2 level 3*

Copy this number sequence. Fill in the missing numbers.

…   …   …   34   37   40   …   …   …

(3) *2006 Progress Test level 3*

a The first odd number is 1.
  What is the sixth odd number?

b The first five odd numbers add up to 25.
  What do the first six odd numbers add up to?

TASK 2: Multiplying and dividing

 Points to remember

- ⊙ 4 × 5 is the same as 5 × 4.
- ⊙ Use a grid to multiply and a 'chunking' method to divide.
- ⊙ Use a calculator to multiply or divide bigger numbers.
- ⊙ Learn multiplication tables by heart.

Do these questions **without a calculator**. Show your working.

1 *2005 level 3*

Copy and complete these calculations to make them correct.
You must use **different numbers** each time.

a ... × ... = 24 **b** ... × ... = 24 **c** ... × ... = 24

2 *2002 level 3*

a Multiply 56 by 3. **b** Divide 130 by 5.

3 *2001 level 3*

Look at this multiplication table.

×	11	12	13	14	15
21	231	252	273	294	315
22	242	264	286	308	330
23	253	276	299	322	345
24	264	288	312	336	360
25	275	300	325	350	375

a Use the table to copy and complete:

24 × 13 = ...

15 × .... = 300

288 ÷ 24 = ...

b Use the table to copy and complete.
Give two different pairs of numbers.

.... × .... = 264

.... × .... = 264

TASK 3: Fractions

$2\frac{1}{4}$ oranges

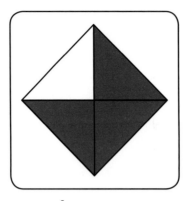

$\frac{3}{4}$ of a square

$\frac{1}{2}$ of a treacle tart

◉ Points to remember

- ⊙ The top number of a fraction is the **numerator**.
  The bottom number is the **denominator**.
- ⊙ If a shape has 8 equal parts and 3 parts are shaded, then $\frac{3}{8}$ is shaded.
- ⊙ Find fractions of numbers by dividing, e.g. to find one third, divide by 3.

1. *2007 Progress Test level 3*

   Look at the shape.
   What fraction of the shape is shaded?

   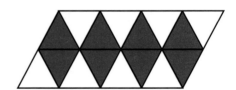

2. *2002 level 3*

   How much of each square grid is shaded?
   For each grid, write **more than half** or **half** or **less than half**.

   a  **b** 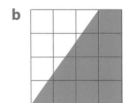 **c**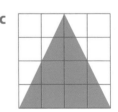

3. *2004 KS1 level 3*

   Copy and complete this sentence to make it correct.

   $$\frac{1}{4} \text{ of } 24 = \frac{1}{2} \text{ of } \ldots\ldots$$

TASK 4: Measures

(1) *2002 KS2 level 3*

Here are a pencil sharpener, a key and an eraser.
What is the total length of all three objects together?

a Write your answer in millimetres only.

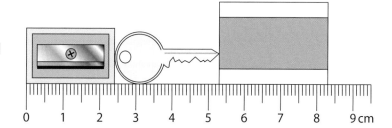

b Write your answers in centimetres and millimetres.

c Write your answer in centimetres only.

(2) *2003 KS2 level 3*

A bottle holds 1 litre of lemonade.
Rachel fills 5 glasses with lemonade.
She puts 100 millilitres in each glass.
How much lemonade is left in the bottle?

(3) *2006 level 3*

A clock shows this time.

a How long is it from this time until 5pm?

b What time was it a quarter of an hour before the time on the clock?

TASK 5: Charts and graphs

Points to remember

⊙ **Carroll diagrams** are used to sort data into groups.
⊙ **Pictograms** use symbols to represent data.

---

1 *2003 KS2 level 3*

Peter and Stella compare colours they like and do not like.
This sorting diagram shows their results.

	Peter likes	Peter does **not** like
Stella likes	red black	orange white
Stella does not like	purple green	yellow

a Write the colours that Stella likes but Peter does not like.

b Peter likes the colour blue but Stella does not.
Write another colour that Peter likes but not Stella.

2 *2005 KS2 level 3*

A shop sells different kinds of greeting cards.
This pictogram shows how many they sold in a week.

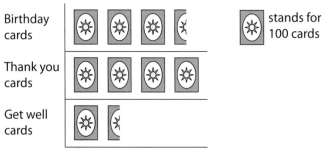

a Estimate how many Birthday cards were sold.

b Estimate how many more Thank You cards than Get Well cards were sold.